BOOK IV
(Grade 5)

THE ASSOCIATED BOARD OF
THE ROYAL SCHOOLS OF MUSIC

Prelude in C minor

PERCY C. BUCK

Scherzetto

HAROLD SAMUEL

In the Bay

FELIX SWINSTEAD

From *Fancy Free*, published by the Associated Board

Peter Squirrel

THOMAS F. DUNHILL

Allegro molto, quasi presto

Knight Errant

JESSIE FURZE

Waking Early on a Summer Morning

SYBIL BARLOW

Pierrot

HUGO ANSON

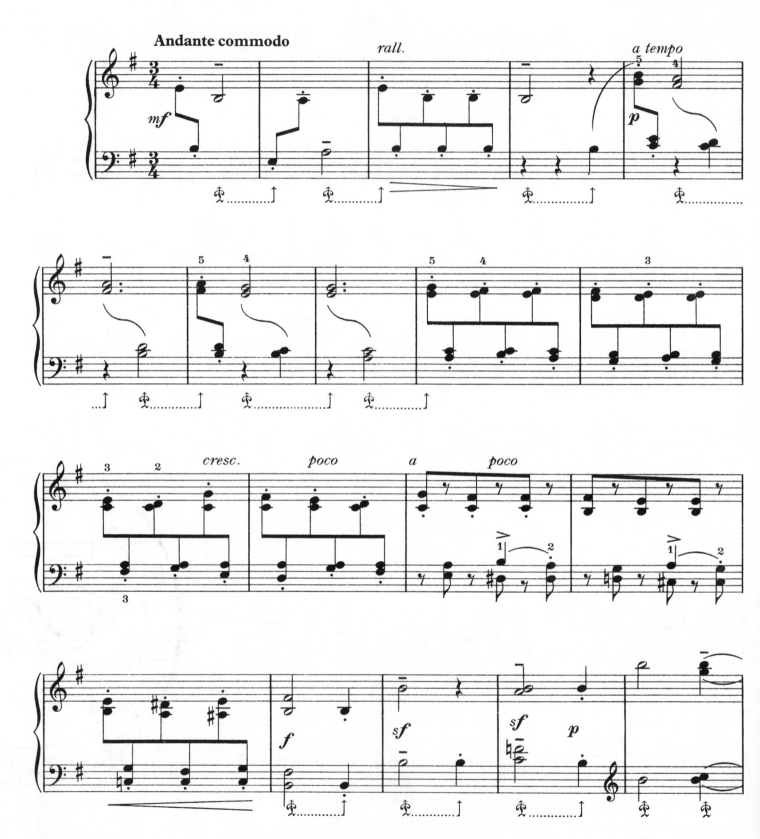

Post Haste

WILLIAM ALWYN

Allegro molto

17

AB 1731

A Wayside Reverie

IVOR R. FOSTER

The Mummers' Dance

HERBERT HOWELLS

With quick but steady pace

From *Country Pageant*, published by the Associated Board

Air and Variations

ALAN RICHARDSON

Poco più mosso

(l'istesso tempo)

cresc.

poco f

più sonore

Berceuse

DAVID GOW

Philomela

DOROTHY PILLING

Andante piangevole

The Elephant's Child

GORDON JACOB

Poco andante

Out of Step

JOSEPH HOROVITZ

Reproduced and printed by
Halstan & Co. Ltd., Amersham, Bucks., England

AB 1731